On the maps in this atlas you will see symbols (little pictures). These show things such as mountains and forests, which wild animals live there, where people work, where they go for holidays and the crops that are grown. This key will help to explain these symbols.

low-lying land
hills
mountains

forests

mountains

crops

wheat and barley

sugar

oranges and lemons

rice

coffee

cotton

apples

timber

tea

tobacco

maize

grapes

bananas

dates

rubber

animals and birds

penguin

giraffe

lion

elephant

zebra

tiger

pig

ostrich

camel

panda

sheep (Africa and Asia)

cows (Africa and Asia)

monkey

buffalo

parrot

koala

sheep (Europe and America)

cows (Europe and America)

bear

kangaroo

shark

llama

seal

reindeer

turtle

where people work

offices

gold mines

precious metals mines

factories

diamond mines

ocean liner

coal mines

fishing

sea port

oil and gas (on land)

oil and gas (at sea)

holidays

skiing

beach holidays

sailing

On several pages in this atlas you will find **Facts and Figures**, and some more symbols. The key below will help to explain what these symbols mean.

total population (how many people live in all the countries shown)

highest peak

longest river

capital city

money

rainfall

temperature

waterfall

desert

lake

cave

Children's ATLAS of the WORLD

Written by Stephen Attmore
Illustrated by George Fryer

*To Mary Jo Anderson
From a Trivial friend Annie
I know it's not round
but it's a start.
Love
Annie
Xmas 1990*

Created and illustrated by Stephen Attmore and George Fryer
courtesy of Bernard Thornton Artists, London.
Copyright © 1989 World International Publishing Limited.
All rights reserved.
Published in Great Britain by World International Publishing Limited,
An Egmont Company, Egmont House,
P.O. Box 111, Great Ducie Street,
Manchester M60 3BL.
Printed in Italy. 1st reprint 1990

British Library Cataloguing in Publication Data

Attmore, Stephen
Children's atlas of the world.
1. World. Atlases.
I. Title II. Fryer, George
912

ISBN 0-7235-2948-5

The colour photographs in this book appear with the kind permission of the following:
page 7 John Mason/ARDEA LONDON; 9TR Orion Press – ZEFA UK; 9B Paulo Koch/VISION INTERNATIONAL; 10 Geoff Tompkinson/ASPECT PICTURE LIBRARY;
11 Frank Lane Picture Agency; 12R Reproduced by permission of the Director, British Geological Survey: Crown Copyright reserved; 12L Adrian Meredith Photography;
13 ZEFA UK; 14 ARDEA LONDON; 15 J Pfaff – ZEFA UK; 16 Gerolf Kalt – ZEFA UK; 19 Peter Carmichael/ASPECT PICTURE LIBRARY; 22 TASS; 23 Novosti Press Agency;
24 ARDEA LONDON; 25T Mark Cator/IMPACT PHOTOS; 25B ARDEA LONDON; 27T M Mann/VISION INTERNATIONAL; 27BL Japan National Tourist Organisation;
27BR The J Allan Cash Photolibrary; 28 Jean-Paul Ferrero/ARDEA LONDON; 30 British Antarctic Survey.

USA
from the Pacific to the Atlantic

The United States' flag is known as the "Stars and Stripes".

ALASKA (1959)
Mt. McKinley
Anchorage

HAWAII (1959)

WASHINGTON (1889)
Mt. St. Helens

OREGON (1859)

CALIFORNIA (1850)

San Francisco

Sequoia National Park

Los Angeles

PACIFIC OCEAN

NEVADA (1864)

IDAHO (1890)

UTAH (1896)

ARIZONA (1912)

Grand Canyon

Missouri

MONTANA (1889)

Rocky Mountain

WYOMING (1890)

COLORADO (1876)

NEW MEXICO (1912)

NORTH DAKOTA (1889)

SOUTH DAKOTA (1889)

NEBRASKA (1867)

KANSAS (1861)

OKLAHOMA (1907)

TEXAS (1845)

The United States of America covers a vast area of land. Long ago, this was the home of Indian tribes. Then people from other parts of the world came to America looking for a new land and settled there.

Until 1775 the thirteen colonies in America belonged to Great Britain. To become independent, the colonies fought Britain in a war that lasted from 1775 to 1783. Once this Revolutionary War was over, America became a new country with its own government and president, George Washington.

When America was settled over 250 years ago, there were thirteen colonies, each with a flag of its own. The flag for the new nation, adopted in 1777, had thirteen stars and stripes, one for each of the colonies. As each new state was accepted into the Union, another star was added. Alaska and Hawaii joined the Union in 1959, bringing to fifty the number of states which now make up the United States of America.

Today the United States is the richest nation in the world with its modern farms, huge cities, and many types of industry.

Cowboys and cowgirls get together to display their skills at **rodeos**. There are contests to see who shoots best with a gun or rifle, who is best at throwing a lasso (rope with a loop) – and perhaps the most famous of all, who can stay on the back of a "bucking bronco" (wild horse).

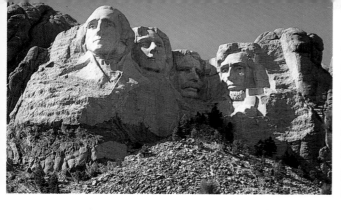

The **Mount Rushmore Sculptures** (1) are four giant heads carved out of the rock – 18 metres (60 feet) high. The faces are of American presidents – George Washington, Thomas Jefferson, Theodore Roosevelt and Abraham Lincoln.

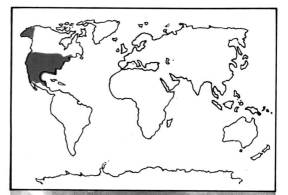

MINNESOTA (1858)
WISCONSIN (1848)
MICHIGAN (1837)
VERMONT (1820)
MAINE (1820)
NEW HAMPSHIRE (1788)
NEW YORK (1788)
MASSACHUSETTS (1788)
IOWA (1846)
Chicago
OHIO (1803)
PENNSYLVANIA (1787)
RHODE ISLAND (1790)
ILLINOIS (1818)
INDIANA (1816)
New York City
CONNECTICUT (1788)
Mammoth Cave
WEST VIRGINIA (1863)
VIRGINIA (1788)
NEW JERSEY (1787)
DELAWARE (1787)
MISSOURI (1821)
KENTUCKY (1792)
4
MARYLAND (1788)
TENNESSEE (1796)
NORTH CAROLINA (1788)
Washington D.C.
ARKANSAS (1836)
GEORGIA (1788)
ATLANTIC OCEAN
MISSISSIPPI (1817)
ALABAMA (1819)
SOUTH CAROLINA (1788)
LOUISIANA (1812)
FLORIDA (1845)
John F Kennedy Space Center
New Orleans
2
Gulf of Mexico

American space rockets are launched into space from the John F Kennedy Space Center (2) in Florida. The **Space Shuttle** was the first spacecraft that could be used again. It flies back to Earth and lands on a runway, just like a plane.

The **roadrunner** lives in the dry deserts of America. It only flies to escape danger. When it moves, it runs to and fro so that it zigzags with its wings outstretched.

Facts and Figures

226.5 million

Washington DC

Missouri – 2nd longest river in the world

A Death Valley – 2nd driest place in the world; only 3mm (0.1 inch) of rain a year.

B Yosemite Falls – 2nd highest waterfall in the world – drop of 739 m (2425 feet).

[The date (in brackets) is the year that state joined the USA.]

Records

Tallest office block – Sears Tower, Chicago – 443 m (1454 feet) high, with 110 storeys (floors) and 16,700 people work there.

Biggest tree in the world – Sequoia tree in Sequoia National Park grows up to 85 m (279 feet) high. (3)

Largest cave system is under Mammoth Cave National Park – maze of caves and passages 307.5 km (191 miles) long. (4)

Scale: 1 cm on the map is really 175 km (109 miles)

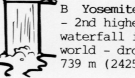

Canada
from the Rockies to the Great Lakes

Canada stretches nearly a quarter of the way around the globe. This vast country is noted for its beautiful scenery from the Rocky Mountains to the Atlantic coastline. The Canadian Shield is a rocky area dotted with thousands of lakes and swamps. In the north the ground is always frozen, so trees and crops cannot grow there. This area is called the **tundra**. The islands in the far north are covered by snow and ice for most of the year. In central Canada, dry grasslands called **prairies** stretch for miles.

The first people to settle in Canada were American Indians who came here more than 20,000 years ago. Most of these Indians lived by hunting buffalo, fishing, and gathering fruit and berries. They made totem poles to guard against evil spirits and lived in teepees.

In 1496 King Henry VII of England sent an explorer named John Cabot to discover new lands and riches. When Cabot reached land, he thought he had gone around the globe to Asia! He called this area the "New Found Land". There is a Canadian province by the same name.

Canada has many natural resources such as oil and fishing areas. It is a member of the British Commonwealth.

Great Bear Lake

Mackenzie

NORTHWEST

Mackenzie Mountains

YUKON TERRITORY

Rocky Mountains

Mt. Logan

ALBERTA

BRITISH COLUMBIA

Edmonton

1

Vancouver

Victoria

SASKATCHEWAN

Roaming the forests in the mountain regions of Canada is the **grizzly bear**. This huge animal can kill creatures bigger than itself with one blow of its paw. A grizzly stands 2.5 metres (8 feet) tall on its hind legs and weighs about 350kg (770lb).

Travel in Canada is usually by road or air. In winter, it is necessary to fit snow chains to car tyres for driving on country roads. In the far north, snow mobiles are used instead of cars. Small **"skidoos"**, like the one above, are a common means of transport in many areas. They look fun. Would you like to own a "skidoo"?

Over 110 years ago, the government in Canada set up a special police force to bring law and order to the western area of the country. They were soon nicknamed the **Mounties**. Can you think why? There is a famous saying: "The Mounties always get their man!" Today they are known as the Royal Canadian Mounted Police. They still wear red jackets and are the only lawmen in the Yukon and Northwest Territories.

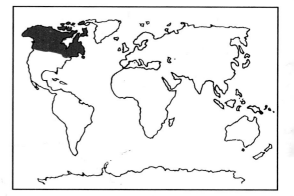

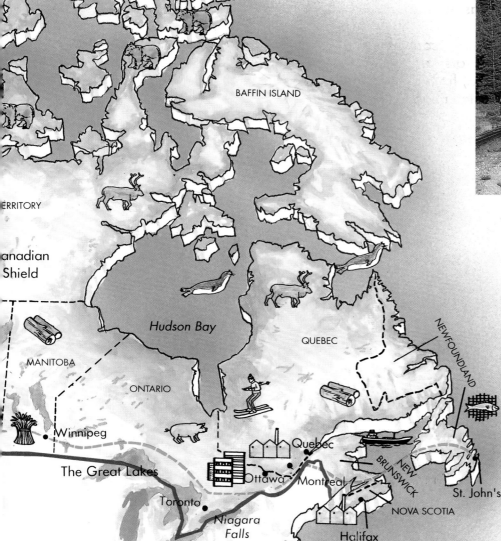

BAFFIN ISLAND

TERRITORY

Canadian
Shield

Hudson Bay

QUEBEC

NEWFOUNDLAND

MANITOBA

ONTARIO

Winnipeg

The Great Lakes

Quebec

Ottawa

Montreal

NEW BRUNSWICK

St. John's

Toronto

Niagara
Falls

NOVA SCOTIA

Halifax

The **Canadian Pacific Railway** runs from coast to coast. The journey from Montreal to Vancouver takes over 70 hours to cover the 4636 km (2860 mile) journey. During the 18th and 19th centuries, Canada was a country of scattered towns and cities. Travel by road was slow, and often impossible in winter. When the Pacific Railway was completed in 1885, the settlements were linked together. (1)

Facts and Figures

Canada – 2nd largest country in the world (after the USSR) – 5500 km (3415 miles) from west coast to east coast.

 about 25 million

Mt Logan (Yukon) – 6050 m (19,850 feet)

 Mackenzie River – 4240 km (2633 miles)

C• Ottawa

 Canadian dollar (= 100 cents)

Winter temperatures below -60°C (-74°F) in far north of Canada

Records

Tallest tower – National Tower, Toronto
Longest road – Trans-Canadian Highway

Scale: 1 cm on map = 235 km (146 miles)

Niagara Falls lies on the border between Canada and the United States. Even though it is not the tallest waterfall in the world, it is the largest. The power of the water is harnessed to produce electricity.

Central and South America
from Mexico to Cape Horn

The continents of North and South America are linked together by a narrow strip of land known as Central America. Central and South America stretch from the hot areas near the equator to the tip of Chile, which is very close to Antarctica.

The area near the Andes Mountains in South America is often shaken by earthquakes and volcanic eruptions. Yet people have settled high in these mountains. La Paz, the capital of Bolivia, is more than 3 kilometres (1.8 miles) above sea level.

Much of South America is dense jungle with small clearings for Indian villages. Yet in many parts of Central and South America, new roads and towns are pushing aside the rain forests and small villages that once stood on the land.

Not all of South America is rain forest. The grasslands of Argentina are called the **pampas**. Men who look after the huge herds of cattle on the ranches are known by the Spanish name **gauchos**. Like the cowboys of North America, the gauchos ride horses and are used to living on their own away from the conveniences of civilization.

Many people in Central and South America farm for a living. Coffee and sugar cane are important crops near the equator, but grain is grown near the southern tip where it is cooler.

Some people in Peru live in the middle of Lake Titicaca (3). By planting reeds they make islands on which they build huts. The totara reed is also used for making boats, bedmats and baskets.

Starting in the 12th century, the **Incas,** a tribe of American Indians, had a huge empire in South America. They built great cities. Some of these were abandoned when the Spanish conquered the Incas during the 16th century. The city of **Machu Pichu** (shown as it is now) was not re-discovered until 1911.

The Incas first settled in the valley of Cuzco, in Peru. A group of tribes started to take over their neighbours. There were many fights between groups of warriors. One group had a king known as the ''Inca''. He was regarded as the child of the sun as the Incas thought of the sun as their god. Part of the land belonged to the Inca himself, and part (one third) to the people. They grew potatoes, beans and maize, and raised animals like the llama and the alpaca. There was a network of straight roads connecting Cuzco with the rest of the empire.

The Incas used a lot of gold and silver in their ornaments. Sadly, many of the treasures they created were melted down by the Spanish conquerors and turned into ingots (blocks of gold or silver).

The **Panama Canal** passes from one side of the country to the other. It provides a vital link for shipping between the Pacific Ocean and the Atlantic Ocean. Before the canal was completed in 1914, silver from Peru was carried across Panama to be loaded into Spanish sailing ships. ''Pirates'' raided the carrying parties and stole the silver.

The **Andean condor** has the largest wing area of any bird – 3 metres (10 feet) from tip to tip. It soars high over the Andes.

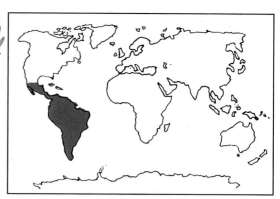

The Bahamas

Cuba

Belize

Jamaica   Haiti

Honduras   *Caribbean Sea*

Dominican Republic

PUERTO RICO

West Indies

Panama Canal

Venezuela

Guyana

Surinam

French Guiana

ATLANTIC OCEAN

Bogota

Columbia

Ecuador

Peru

Lima

Andes Mountains

Cuzco

3.

Bolivia

La Paz

Lake Poopo

PACIFIC OCEAN

Paraguay

Amazon

Tropical Rain Forest

Brazil

Brasilia

Rio de Janeiro

2

Argentina

Chile

Mt. Aconcagua

Santiago

Andes Mountains

Buenos Aires

Uruguay

Montevideo

FALKLAND ISLANDS

Cape Horn

1

It rains almost every day in parts of central Brazil. Forests grow tall and dense, blocking out the sunlight. Tribes of Indians live deep in the Amazon jungle. For food they shoot small animals and birds using blowguns. They dip the heads of their darts onto poison from the skin of the **arrow poison frog**.

Facts and Figures

Total: 262 million

Mt Aconcagua – 6960 m (22,835 feet)

[The Andes – longest chain of mountains in the world.]

Amazon – world's largest river – 6448 km (4007 miles)

1 **Angel Falls** – highest waterfall in the world – 979 m (3212 feet) high

2 **Guaira Falls** – nearly 5 km (3 miles) across

3 **Lake Titicaca** – highest inland sea in the world

Scale: 1 cm on the map is really 325 km (200 miles)

The British Isles
from Shetland to Land's End

The British Isles are the two large islands and several smaller ones off the coast of northwest Europe. The United Kingdom of Great Britain and Northern Ireland consists of four of the countries on the islands: England, Scotland, Wales, and Northern Ireland. All of Ireland was once part of the United Kingdom, but now the Republic of Ireland is independent.

The British Isles were invaded many times. The Romans were the first to conquer, building the famous Hadrian's Wall that separated the tribes in Scotland from those in England. The Romans were soon followed by other conquerors: Saxons, Vikings, Danes, and Normans. With each new group of invaders, the English language changed to include new words and ideas of the invaders.

Many areas in the British Isles are very thickly populated and industrialized. The Industrial Revolution of the 1700s began in the United Kingdom, but since the end of World War II, the United Kingdom has been overtaken by the United States and the Soviet Union.

Other areas of Britain and Ireland are known for agriculture and livestock. In fact, the fields of Ireland are so green that Ireland has long been known as the Emerald Isle.

The United Kingdom flag is called the **Union Jack**. It is made up of the flags of England (white with a large red cross), Scotland (blue with white cross) and Ireland (red cross from corner to corner).

Concorde is the fastest passenger aircraft. Powered by four turbo jet engines, the plane cruises at a speed of 2300km/h (1450mph). It has a pointed nose and wings shaped like triangles. The nose is lowered for take-off and landing, to give the pilot a better view of the runway. The first Concorde flew in 1969.

NORTHERN Belfast
IRELAND

Shannon

Dublin

Republic of Ireland

Carrauntoohill

A ship in distress sent an SOS signal to the coastguard. A lifeboat and a helicopter have come to the rescue.

Land's En

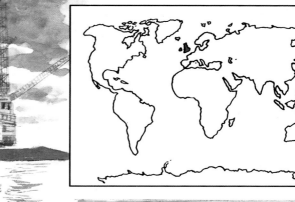

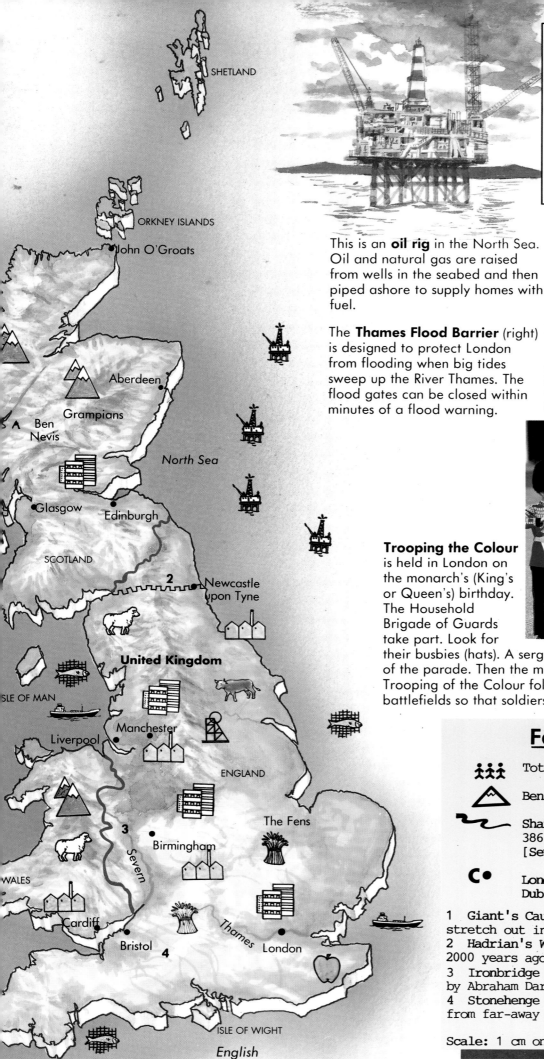

This is an **oil rig** in the North Sea. Oil and natural gas are raised from wells in the seabed and then piped ashore to supply homes with fuel.

The **Thames Flood Barrier** (right) is designed to protect London from flooding when big tides sweep up the River Thames. The flood gates can be closed within minutes of a flood warning.

Trooping the Colour is held in London on the monarch's (King's or Queen's) birthday. The Household Brigade of Guards take part. Look for their busbies (hats). A sergeant bears the Colour (flag) to the front of the parade. Then the monarch inspects the Guards. The Trooping of the Colour follows. "Colours" were carried on to battlefields so that soldiers knew where their regiment was.

Facts and Figures

👥👥 Total: over 58 million

△ Ben Nevis – 1343 m (4406 feet)

〰 Shannon (Republic of Ireland) – 386 km (240 miles) [Severn – 354 km (220 miles)]

C● London (UK) Dublin (Republic of Ireland)

1 **Giant's Causeway** - over 32,000 stone columns stretch out into the sea
2 **Hadrian's Wall** - built by the Romans nearly 2000 years ago [117 km (72 miles) long]
3 **Ironbridge** - world's 1st iron bridge; built by Abraham Darby III in 1779
4 **Stonehenge** - circle of giant stones brought from far-away places thousands of years ago

Scale: 1 cm on the map is really 43.5 km (27 miles)

Northern Europe
from the Arctic Ocean to Liechtenstein

Northern Europe stretches from the cold lands of the north to the inland countries in the centre of the continent of Europe. The countries are of varied cultures, languages, and sizes. Some, such as Sweden and Poland, are very large; yet some, such as Liechtenstein, are tiny.

Scandinavia is the name given to the countries of Norway, Sweden, Finland, and Denmark. Forests and lakes cover much of Scandinavia. The Scandinavian people have found ways of using these natural resources. Trees are cut down and the logs are floated down the lakes and rivers to timber mills. As well as fishing in the North Sea, the Norwegians also drill for oil and gas. The energy of water as it rushes over waterfalls is changed into electricity, producing enough power to heat all the nearby houses.

Denmark includes over 500 islands, but only about 100 are inhabited. Fishing is an important industry along the coastline of Denmark, Germany, and Poland. In the inland areas, many different types of agriculture, livestock and dairy farming, mining, and manufacturing provide a variety of employment opportunities for the people.

From the plains in the north of Poland and Germany, the countryside changes to rolling hills in the southern areas and finally becomes the rocky mountain peaks of the Austrian Alps.

In summer in Scandinavia the sun shines all night long. In winter it is dark all day. This photograph was taken in Norway at midnight in summer.

This castle was built for King Ludwig II of Bavaria. It was completed in 1886, just before the king drowned in a nearby lake. The marble building stands on a large crag (rock) near the Bavarian Alps in West Germany. The castle cost 6 million gold Marks to build. It looks like a castle from a fairy tale.

Republic of Ireland

United Kingdom

North Sea

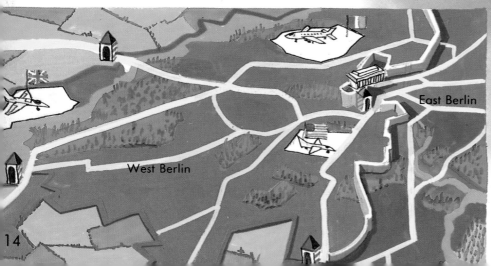

East Berlin

West Berlin

After World War II, Germany was split into two – West Germany and East Germany. The **Berlin Wall** was built to divide the old capital city, East and West. The map (left) shows the main roads out of East Berlin, guarded by checkpoints. Now the two countries are working towards reunification.

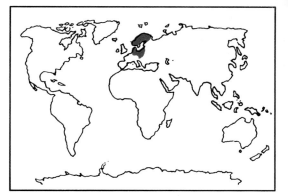

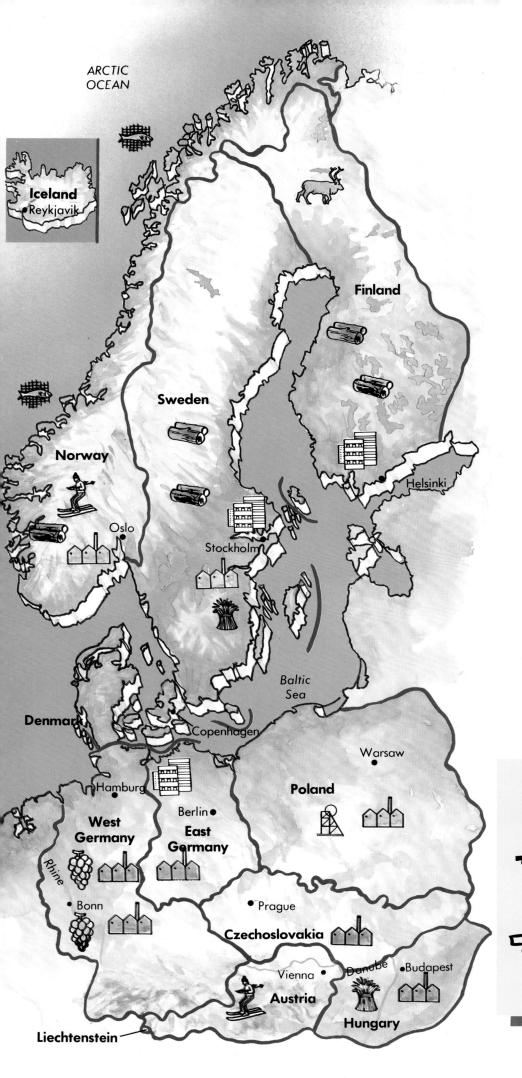

ARCTIC
OCEAN

Iceland
• Reykjavik

Finland

Sweden

Norway

Oslo

Stockholm

Helsinki

*Baltic
Sea*

Denmark

Copenhagen

Warsaw

Hamburg

Poland

Berlin •

**West
Germany**

**East
Germany**

Rhine

• Bonn

• Prague

Czechoslovakia

Danube

Vienna •

• Budapest

Austria

Hungary

Liechtenstein

Hans Christian Andersen (1805-75) was a Danish writer of stories. One of his tales is about the **Little Mermaid**. A bronze statue of the mermaid sits on a rock near the shore of Copenhagen.

If you look at the map, you will see that the coast of Norway is uneven. This is because the coast is full of steep-sided valleys called **fjords**.

Facts and Figures

Total: 161 million

Danube – 2850 km (1770 miles) – flows through 3 capital cities and through 6 countries in all. [Rhine –2nd longest river – 1320 km (825 miles)]

Finland has 55,000 lakes.

Scale: 1 cm on the map is really 100 km (62 miles)

Southern Europe
from the Netherlands to the Mediterranean

The countries from the Netherlands to the tip of Sicily make up Southern Europe. Southern Europe has great mountain ranges such as the Alps with steep jagged peaks. On the other hand, much of the land of the Netherlands, Holland, and Belgium was once completely underwater. For the past several hundred years, the people of these countries have built large dams called dykes that push the ocean back, leaving dry land for farming and manufacturing.

There are many different types of industry to be found in Southern Europe in addition to manufacturing. France is a great producer of wine and cheese. Nearly half the people in Portugal work on farms or in the cork forests. The city of Rotterdam in the Netherlands is one of the world's largest ports.

Tourism is also a very important industry. From skiing in the Alps to sunning on the beaches, Southern Europe has holiday spots for every season of the year. Italy and Greece are very interesting to visit because of the ancient art treasures that are preserved there.

The **Vatican** in Rome is the smallest state in the world. The head of this tiny state is the Pope. Only 1000 people live in the Vatican. Outside the Pope's palace you find the Swiss Guard.

The French high-speed train **TGV-PSE** holds the record for any train on a national rail system. It travels the 425km (264 miles) between Paris and Lyon in 2 hours, reaching speeds of 270 km/h (168 mph).

The solar (sun) power station at **Odeillo** makes electricity that is used all over France. The mirrors reflect sunlight on to a furnace. Temperatures in the furnace reach nearly 4000°C (7532°F).

The **rock of Gibraltar** is at the southern tip of Spain and guards the entrance to the Mediterranean. It became a British colony in 1704. Now it is claimed by Spain. Troops of **Barbary apes** live on the "rock". Between 10 and 30 of them live together. These tail-less apes sleep in trees or on rocks.

The **Parthenon** is in Athens (Greece). It was built as a temple to the Greek goddess Athena over 2400 years ago. In 1687 the Parthenon was destroyed when the city of Athens was attacked.

Rotterdam • Amsterdam
Netherlands
Brussels •
1
Belgium
Seine
Luxembourg
Paris •
3
France
Switzerland
Mt Blanc
Geneva
2
Venice •
The Alps
Lyon •
Italy
Pyrenees
Andorra
CORSICA
Rome •
SARDINIA
MAJORCA
Mediterranean Sea
SICILY

Romania
Belgrade •
Danube
Yugoslavia
Bulgaria
Sofia •
Adriatic Sea
Tirana •
Albania
Greece
Athens •

Venice, in Italy, is the only city in the world that has no roads. It only has canals and footpaths. The boats are called **gondolas**.

Facts and Figures

Total: 241 million

Mount Blanc (France) – 4807 m (15,770 feet)

Temperatures in Athens range from 6–13°C (43–55 F) in February to 23–33°C (73–91°F) in July.

1 Brussels – headquarters of the European Economic Community (EEC).
2 St Gotthard Tunnel in Switzerland is the world's longest road tunnel – 16.32 km (10.14 miles) long.
3 Eiffel Tower – built for the Paris exhibition of 1889. It is 300 m (985 feet) tall and sways 12.7cm (5 inches) in strong winds.

Scale: 1 cm on the map is really 113 km (70 miles)

Africa
from Mediterranean to Cape of Good Hope

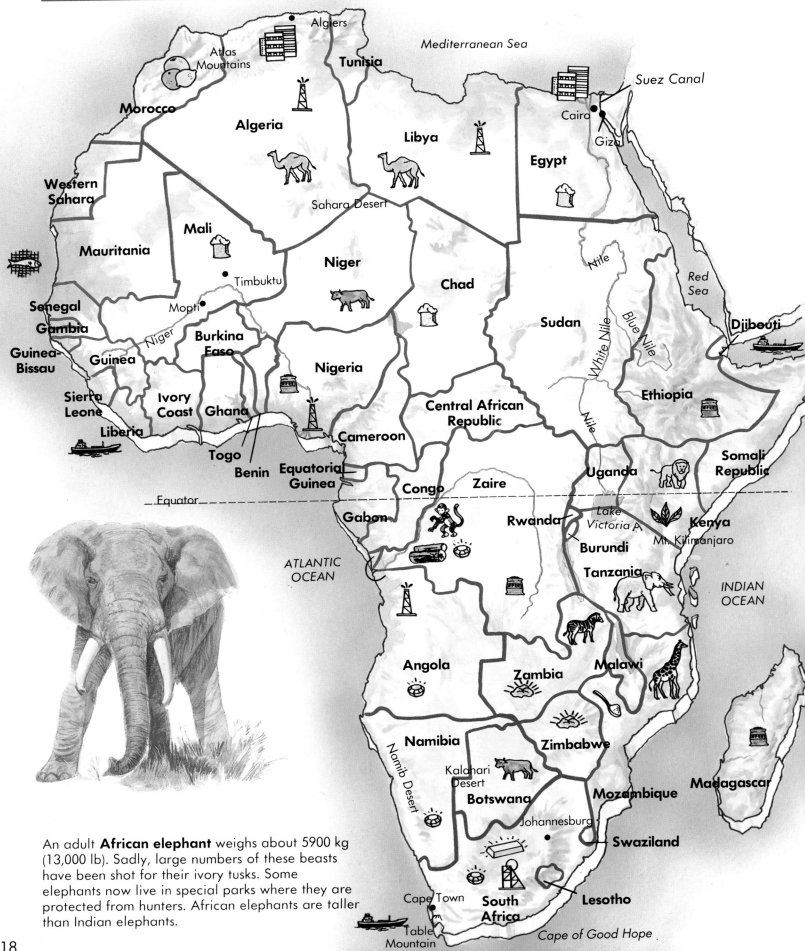

Mediterranean Sea

Algiers

Atlas Mountains

Tunisia

Morocco

Algeria

Libya

Suez Canal

Cairo

Giza

Egypt

Western Sahara

Sahara Desert

Mauritania

Mali

Timbuktu

Niger

Chad

Nile

Red Sea

Mopti

Sudan

Djibouti

Senegal

Gambia

Niger

Burkina Faso

White Nile

Blue Nile

Guinea-Bissau

Guinea

Nigeria

Ethiopia

Sierra Leone

Ivory Coast

Ghana

Central African Republic

Nile

Liberia

Togo

Benin

Cameroon

Somali Republic

Equatorial Guinea

Congo

Zaire

Uganda

Kenya

Equator

Gabon

Rwanda

Lake Victoria

Mt. Kilimanjaro

Burundi

ATLANTIC OCEAN

Tanzania

INDIAN OCEAN

Angola

Zambia

Malawi

Namibia

Zimbabwe

Namib Desert

Kalahari Desert

Mozambique

Madagascar

Botswana

Johannesburg

Cape Town

Swaziland

South Africa

Lesotho

Table Mountain

Cape of Good Hope

An adult **African elephant** weighs about 5900 kg (13,000 lb). Sadly, large numbers of these beasts have been shot for their ivory tusks. Some elephants now live in special parks where they are protected from hunters. African elephants are taller than Indian elephants.

18

The continent of Africa is the second largest in the world. The equator cuts Africa almost exactly in half. Near the equator it is very hot. There are humid jungles and wide **savannas**, or grass plains. In the north the land is mostly hot, dry desert.

Many exotic animals, such as lions and giraffes, live in Africa. These animals live in the savannas and are protected in some of the world's finest game reserves in Kenya, Tanzania, South Africa, and other countries.

Africa is also the site of early great civilizations. The Egyptian empire flourished nearly 5,000 years ago. Many trading empires sprang up in North Africa. They shipped their goods in long camel caravans across the Sahara Desert. The Portuguese were the first European explorers to begin charting the African coast in the 1600s. Yet no one mapped the interior until the 1800s when explorers such as David Livingstone began to explore it.

By 1920 nearly all of Africa had been claimed by various European countries. But in the 1950s, African countries began to seek independence. Today the countries are ruled by the people.

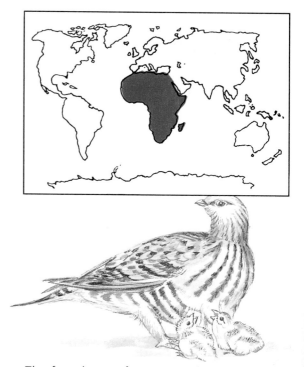

The **Sahara** is a huge area of dry land that is hot all year round. At Kebili the temperature has been recorded at 55°C (131°F). In the Sahara it is very hot by day and cold at night. Few people live there because there are no animals to hunt and few plants that can be eaten. But they do pass through it. The **Tuareg** take bronze, dates and cloth down to Timbuktu and Mopti and bring back salt. Even they could not manage these trips without the aid of camels. The one-humped camels of the Sahara are suited to life in the desert. They can survive for long periods without water. Yet even a camel cannot travel through the Sahara without the Tuareg men to haul buckets of water up from wells.

The female **sandgrouse** makes a nest in the Kalahari Desert in Botswana. Each day she leaves the young birds to fly many miles in search of water. She soaks up the water in her breast feathers before flying back. The young suck the wet feathers for a drink.

Did you know that both the tallest and the shortest groups of people in the world live in Africa? The herdsmen of **Rwanda** and **Burundi** are nearly all 183cm (6ft) tall. **Mbuti pygmies** live in the Zaire forests. Their average height is 132cm (4.3ft).

This giant statue at Giza in Egypt has a lion's body, but the head of a man. It is the **Sphinx** which is 4500 years old – one of the most famous monuments in the world. Behind the Sphinx you can see a pyramid. These were built from millions of stone slabs. They took years to build. Inside are chambers where the Pharoahs and Queens were buried.

Facts and Figures

Total: 484 million

Mt Kilimanjaro (Tanzania) – 5895 m (19,340 feet)

Nile – world's longest river – 6695 km (4160 miles)

Sahara – world's largest desert – 5150 km (3200 miles) wide

Scale: 1 cm on the map is really 315 km (195 miles)

Middle East
from the Black Sea to the Red Sea

The countries from Turkey to Iran make up the Middle East. This area is mainly desert and plains. Weather in the Middle East is mostly hot and dry, with less than ten centimetres of rain a year in some desert areas. During the daytime in these deserts, it is very hot, but the nights are very cold.

One third of the world's oil comes from countries in the Middle East. Selling this oil has made some countries very rich. But farming is still the main source of employment in the areas that are not too hot and dry. Much of Israel's farming is based on the **kibbutz** system. The kibbutz is a collective farm. Everyone helps with the work, earnings are shared equally, and food and housing are provided.

Three of the world's religions are centered in the Middle East. Israel is the promised land of the Jews. Jerusalem is an important city for Jews, Christians, and Muslims. Yet Mecca is the most holy city for Muslims. This city was the birthplace of Mohammed, the founder of Islam. One of the goals of every Muslim is to go on a pilgrimage, or religious journey, to Mecca at least one time in their lives. Over one million pilgrims visit Mecca each year, travelling there from countries all over the world.

Jerusalem is the capital of the modern state of Israel. The golden **Dome of the Rock** can be seen from all over the city. This mosque (temple) was built by the Muslims who invaded in 638 AD. In front is the **Western Wall**. This is all that remains of a temple destroyed by the Romans over 2000 years ago. It is also known as "Wailing Wall" because of the sound of Jewish prayers being chanted.

The largest ship in the world is an oil tanker called *Seawise Giant*. It is 458 metres (1500 feet) long and weighs 564,739 tonnes.

The **Dead Sea** has so much salt in it that no plants or fish can live there. Why is it so salty? As it is cut off by land, the only way it loses water is by evaporation. When water evaporates into the air, it leaves behind salt. The Dead Sea is so salty that swimmers do not sink.

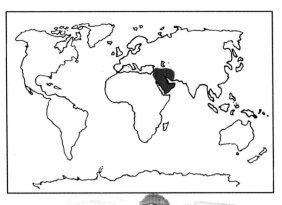

Mt. Ararat

Caspian Sea

Tehran

Tigris

Iraq

Baghdad

Euphrates

Iran

Kuwait

Persian Gulf

Bahrain

(Oman)

Qatar

Saudi Arabia

United Arab Emirates

Riyadh

Muscat

Arabian Sea

Mecca

Oman

Rub Al Khali ("Empty Quarter")

Yemen Arab Republic

People's Democratic Republic of Yemen

Aden

INDIAN OCEAN

Every country has a police force. This is a **police officer** in Saudi Arabia. Look at his headgear. This type of head clothing is worn by many people in the Middle East to protect their heads from the sun. This police officer is on a one-humped camel. In countries like Arabia, camel racing is a very popular sport.

This house in the Middle East has no windows. There is only a small opening near the top of the wind tower. Any breeze goes down the tower into the house to cool the inside. The thick walls also help to keep it cool inside.

Facts and Figures

Total: 150 million

Mt Ararat (Turkey) – 5165 m (16,946 feet) – where Noah's Ark landed after the Flood

Euphrates – 2720 km (1690 miles)

Rub Al Khali (means "Empty Quarter") is 4th largest desert in world. [Highest temperature ever recorded in Asia was 53.8°C (129°F) in Israel.]

Scale: 1 cm on the map = 205 km (127 miles)

USSR
from the Baltic to the Bering

The Union of Soviet Socialist Republics, or USSR, is the largest country in the world. It is more than twice the size of Canada, the second largest. Fifteen republics belong to the Soviet Union.

Despite the size of the Soviet Union, only ten percent of the land can be used to grow food. Additional food must be imported because the farmers cannot grow enough to feed everyone. The Soviet Union does have many natural resources. The USSR is the world's leading producer of petroleum products, coal, iron ore, and timber.

Most of the population lives in the lands west of the Ural Mountains. Most of the crops are grown here in the flat grasslands called **steppes**. Very few people live in the cold, treeless tundra areas of the north or the desert regions of the south.

The tsars, or emperors, of Russia ruled from the city of St. Petersburg, now called Leningrad. Then in 1917 the tsar was overthrown in a revolution. Russia and several other countries joined together to become the Soviet Union under new leaders, Lenin and Trotsky.

Since 1922 the population of the Soviet Union has doubled in size. Over one thousand new towns have been built. New developments in industry have made the Soviet Union one of the most powerful nations in the world.

This statue was erected in 1937 near Moscow. It is called the "Worker and Collective Farmer" and is over 76m (250 feet) tall. Look for the tools the man and woman are holding. The hammer and sickle also appear on the Union of Soviet Socialist Republics' flag.

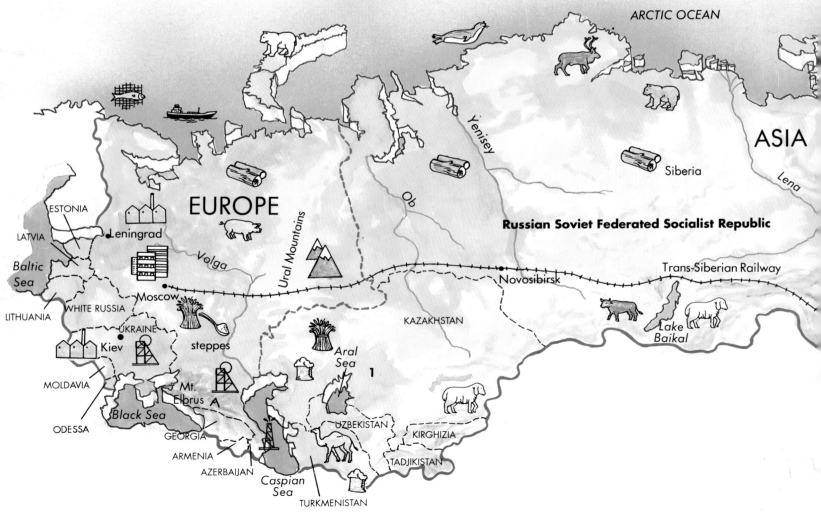

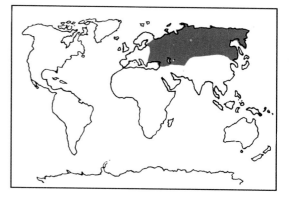

The **Kremlin** is a group of buildings in Moscow that were once the home of the Russian tsars. Now the Communist Party and the Russian government hold meetings there. The Kremlin has high walls around it. **Red Square** is a broad, open space about 400 metres (437 yards) long. It is best known for the huge parades held there on May Day. The tomb of Lenin, founder of modern USSR, is in front of the Kremlin.

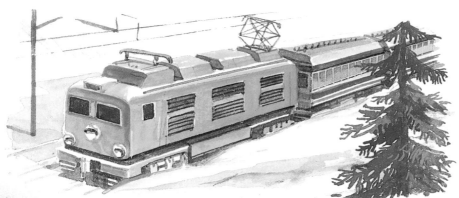

The longest railway track in the world is the **Trans-Siberian Railway**. The distance from Moscow to Vladivostock is 9438km (5964 miles). There are 97 stops on the journey which lasts for eight days and four hours (if it's not late!).

In April 1961 **Yuri Gagarin** (top left) was the first person to travel in Space. He went once around the Earth in "Vostock 1". The first woman in space was **Valentina Tereshkova** (top right). She travelled in "Vostock 6" (above) in 1963. Russians call people who travel in space **cosmonauts**. (See Space Launching Centre, 1 on map.)

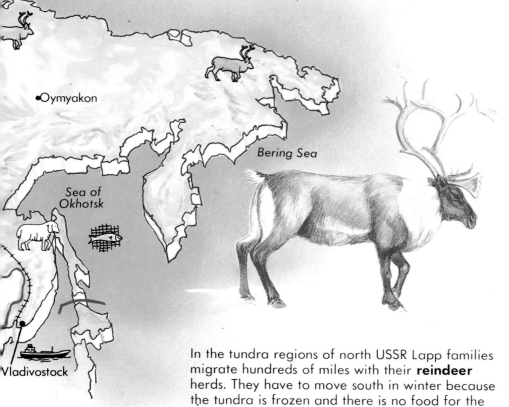

In the tundra regions of north USSR Lapp families migrate hundreds of miles with their **reindeer** herds. They have to move south in winter because the tundra is frozen and there is no food for the reindeer.

Facts and Figures

👥👥👥	Total: 280 million
🔺	Mt Elbrus – 5642 m (18,481 feet)
〰	Volga – 3688 km (2293 miles)
C•	Moscow
💰	rouble (= 100 kopeks)
🏞	Caspian Sea – world's largest lake Lake Baikal – world's deepest lake
🌡	– 78°C (–108°F) at Oymyakon is lowest recorded temperature in USSR.

Scale: 1 cm on the map is really 264 km (165 miles)

Asia
from Karachi to Beijing

The continent of Asia is a land of contrasts. The highest mountains in the world are in the Himalayas, but vast stretches of plains are completely flat. Rain falls almost daily in the wet jungles, but the Gobi Desert is very dry. Mongolian winters are extremely cold, but India is very hot.

The weather is also unpredictable. In southern farming areas, long droughts, or periods without rain, will cause all the crops to die. Yet sometimes there can be serious floods which sweep away houses and farms, and drown the crops. Often the people cannot grow enough food to eat.

In addition to farming, many Asian countries are very industrialized. Many people in China, Taiwan, and Korea work in factories.

Religions such as Buddhism, Hinduism, and Sikhism are the most popular in Asia. Hindus believe that the Ganges River is so holy it will stay clean forever. In India cows are sacred. They are not killed for meat, and can roam the streets!

Some boys in Nepal and Bhutan go to special schools from the age of five to train as monks. They get up at five in the morning to pray and meditate before lessons begin. The boys' heads are shaved.

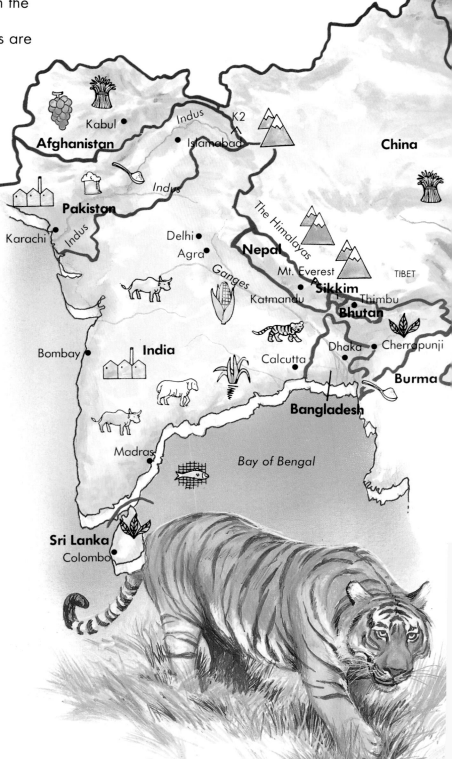

The **Taj Mahal** stands outside the city of Agra in India. Emperor Shah Jahan ordered it to be built in memory of his wife, Mumtaz Mahal. It took 20,000 workers 20 years to build the white marble building.

The **tiger** (right) is the largest of the big cats. This powerful animal lives in the wild in India, Nepal and Bangladesh. Tigers kill about 30 times in a year. They eat between 18 and 23kg (40-50lb) in one meal.

In many Asian cities, the **rickshaw** is used as a taxi to take people from place to place. Some are pulled by a person running, others are pulled by a rider on a bicycle. Here the rickshaws are passing an open market in Katmandu.

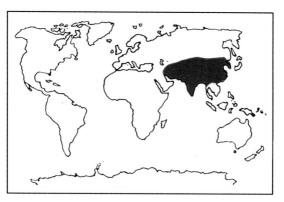

Over 5 million people live in buildings in Hong Kong. There is even a floating village of 4000 homes, shops and temples. Families live on boats known as **junks**. Flat-bottomed boats called **sampans** are used for fishing.

Mongolia

Ulan Bator

Gobi Desert

(Inner Mongolia)

1

Pyongyang

North Korea

Beijing (Peking)

2

Seoul

South Korea

Yellow Sea

Shanghai

Yangtze Kiang

East China Sea

Taipei

Hong Kong

Taiwan

Facts and Figures

Total: 1945 million

Mt Everest and K2 – highest mountains in the world:
Everest – 8848 m (29,029 feet)
K2 – 8611 m (28,250 feet)

Yangtze – 3rd longest river in world – 6380 km (3965 miles)

Most rain in 1 month: 929 cm (30 feet) at Cherrapunji (India)

1 Great Wall – only man-made structure on Earth that can be seen from Space. Built over 2200 years ago, it is 6325 km (3930 miles) long.

2 Hwang Ho (means "yellow river") – China's 2nd longest river – carries silt (pieces of fine rock) that stains the river water and the sea yellow.

Scale: 1 cm on the map is really 200 km (124 miles)

Rice is the staple diet in Asian countries. The fields are flooded to grow the rice. They are called **paddy-fields**. Monsoons (heavy rains) come in the months from June to September. These workers are wearing straw shields to keep the rain off as they plant out the rice.

Japan and South East Asia
Indo-China and assorted islands

The area we call South East Asia includes the countries in Indo-China and over 20,000 islands that lie between Asia and Australia. Tropical rain forests cover much of South East Asia. The people who live there must contend with very strong winds called **typhoons**, earthquakes, and the occasional erupting volcano.

Hundreds of years ago, European traders came to these islands. The oils and spices that they bought could be sold for large amounts of money in Europe. Many people became very rich as traders.

Today there are huge cities in South East Asia and Japan. Some are very beautiful. The city of Singapore is known as "City of Lions" or the "Garden City". Singapore is also called "Instant Asia" because the population consists of a mix of Chinese, Malaysian, and Indian people.

Millions of people in South East Asia leave the country and move to cities in search of work. Often they find that the cities are crowded and the people who live there are very poor.

Japan is a very important manufacturing nation, famous for the electrical goods, cars, bikes, and toys that are built there. Smoke and dust from the factories often fills the air of huge cities like Tokyo. Japanese workers work more hours each day and more days each year than people in most other countries.

Key

1 **Marianas Trench** is the deepest ocean in the world. If Mt Everest was dropped into the sea here it would not show above the water. This trench is 10,900 m deep (nearly 7 miles).

2 The **longest bridge in the world** links the Japanese islands of Honshu and Shikoku. It is a road-rail bridge 3560 m (11,680 feet) long.

3 **Krakatoa** is a small island between Java and Sumatra. It is what remains of a much larger volcano which erupted in 1883 with a very big bang. A dust cloud formed which stretched 80.5 km (50 miles) up in the air. The island sank into the sea creating a huge wave.

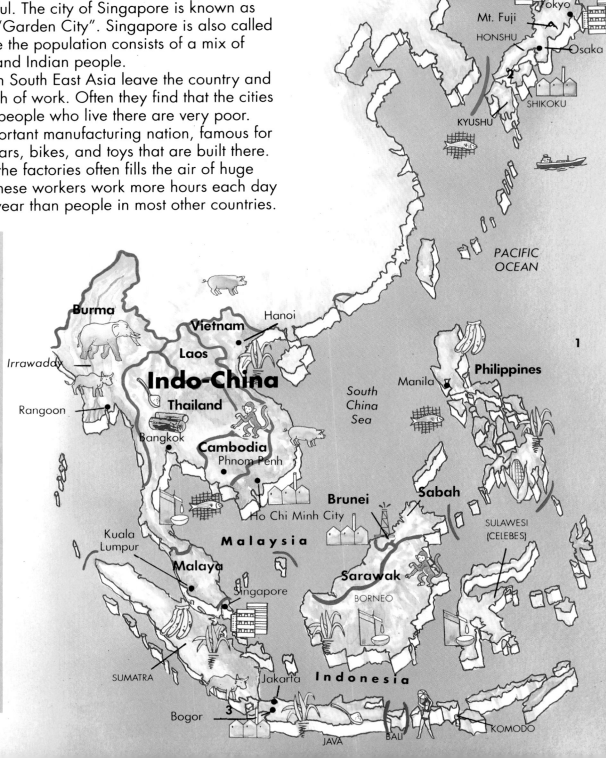

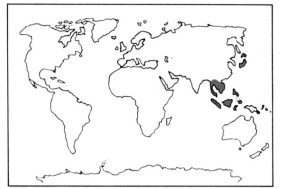

The **Komodo dragon** is the largest lizard in the world. As there are no animals on the island of Komodo that attack the lizard, it does not have to run away, hide or change colour. The "dragon" just grows bigger and bigger. Males are 3 metres (10 feet) long and use their strong jaws and large claws to kill deer and pigs.

Rubber trees in South East Asia provide natural rubber. A cut is made in the tree bark and a cup is tied on to collect the rubber that oozes out.

Klongs are canals in Bangkok, capital city of Thailand. There is a market on one of the canals. Some people come here in small boats to buy fruit and vegetables and others come to the water's edge.

The **Golden Pagoda** is a temple which sits on top of a hill by Rangoon, capital city of Burma. A layer of gold covers the building from top to bottom. At Buddhist festivals, people from all over Burma come here to say prayers at the foot of the Golden Pagoda.

Tokyo is the biggest city in the world. Nearly 12 million people live and work there. The city was first founded over 500 years ago with the name of Edo. It was renamed Tokyo in 1868. An earthquake shook the city in 1923. About 100,000 people were killed.

Kite fights take place in Japan and Thailand each year in May. The teams try to destroy the other team's kite by ramming their kite into it.

Facts and Figures

👪 Total: 362 million

⛰ Mt Fuji – Japan's highest peak – 3776 m (12,389 feet)

〰 Irrawaddy (Burma) – about 2000 km (1250 miles) long

🌧 Bogor (Java) has thunder storms on 322 days each year.

Scale: 1 cm on the map is really 284.5 km (176.5 miles)

Australasia
Australia and lots of other islands

Australia is the smallest of the continents. This continent includes the country of Australia, the island countries of New Zealand and Papua New Guinea, and many other small island nations in the Pacific Ocean.

When the English explorer Captain James Cook arrived on the shores of Australia over 200 years ago, the only people living there were the Aborigines. Eighty years later, the discovery of gold in Australia brought colonists from all over the world. Now there are also silver, zinc, iron, and diamond mines in Australia.

Australia is also home to some unique animals that are found nowhere else in the world. The kangaroo, koala, and platypus can only be found in Australia. Australia is also now the home of large herds of sheep, over 138 million of them.

Finding water can be a real problem in some areas of Australia, the driest of all the continents. The centre of Australia, called the **outback**, can be very hot. Most of the people live along the coasts where it is cooler. Even though Australia is the sixth largest country in the world, its average population density, number of people per square kilometre, is very low. Huge areas of Australia are almost completely empty.

This picture shows **Aborigines** from Arnhem Land in the Northern Territory performing a "spear dance".

There are hot springs and geysers in parts of New Zealand. Geysers shoot a jet of boiling water and steam high into the air.

Darwin
Arnhem Land
NORTHERN TERRITORY
Great Sandy Desert
Australia
Alice Springs
WESTERN AUSTRALIA
SOUTH AUSTRALIA
Perth

koala
kangaroo

Key
1 **Ayers Rock** – largest block of stone in the world (1100ft/335m high, 2 miles/3.2km long). It is over 230 million years old and is made of red sandstone.

2 **Wave Rock** – over hundreds of years the wind, sand and rain have shaped the rock. It looks like a giant frozen wave.

3 **Wairakei** – when water seeps down deep to where the earth is very hot, it is pushed up again and comes out as a hot spring. Sometimes the hot water makes pools of bubbling hot mud.

4 The **largest sheep farm** in the world is at Commonwealth Hill. Nearly 70,000 sheep graze there.

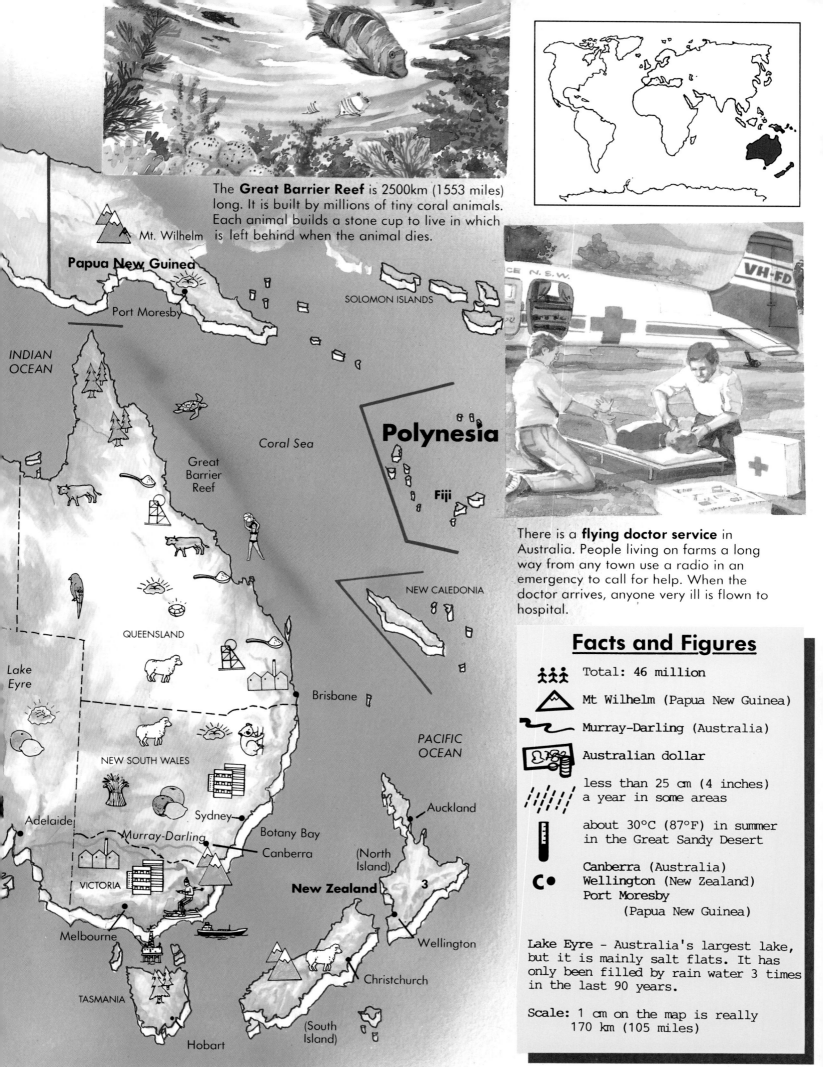

The **Great Barrier Reef** is 2500km (1553 miles) long. It is built by millions of tiny coral animals. Each animal builds a stone cup to live in which is left behind when the animal dies.

Mt. Wilhelm

Papua New Guinea

Port Moresby

SOLOMON ISLANDS

INDIAN OCEAN

Polynesia

Coral Sea

Great Barrier Reef

Fiji

QUEENSLAND

Lake Eyre

NEW CALEDONIA

Brisbane

PACIFIC OCEAN

NEW SOUTH WALES

Adelaide

Murray-Darling

Sydney

Botany Bay

Canberra

Auckland

(North Island)

VICTORIA

New Zealand

Melbourne

Wellington

Christchurch

TASMANIA

(South Island)

Hobart

There is a **flying doctor service** in Australia. People living on farms a long way from any town use a radio in an emergency to call for help. When the doctor arrives, anyone very ill is flown to hospital.

Facts and Figures

Total: 46 million

Mt Wilhelm (Papua New Guinea)

Murray-Darling (Australia)

Australian dollar

less than 25 cm (4 inches) a year in some areas

about 30°C (87°F) in summer in the Great Sandy Desert

Canberra (Australia)
Wellington (New Zealand)
Port Moresby
(Papua New Guinea)

Lake Eyre - Australia's largest lake, but it is mainly salt flats. It has only been filled by rain water 3 times in the last 90 years.

Scale: 1 cm on the map is really 170 km (105 miles)

The Arctic...

The world is like a spinning ball. At the very top, there is a point that does not appear to move. On the earth, this point is called the **North Pole**. Around that point is the area known as the Arctic, a huge block of ice. The Arctic also includes the northern parts of Canada, Alaska, Siberia, and Greenland, a large island belonging to Denmark.

Temperatures in the Arctic are always below freezing. There is no day or night at the North Pole. In the winter the North Pole is tilted away from the sun, so it is dark twenty-four hours a day. In the summer the North Pole is tilted towards the sun so it is always light. But because the sun is so low in the sky, its rays do not warm the air very much.

The North Pole was first reached in 1909 by the American explorer Robert Peary.

The **polar bear** is well adapted for life in the Arctic. The bear's coat keeps it warm and enables it to hide. This polar bear is waiting beside a seal's breathing hole.

Where the ice meets the sea, huge blocks break off. These are called **icebergs**. We see only the tip of an iceberg above the water. Arctic icebergs are high and jagged. Icebergs in the Antarctic are mostly flat topped (below). The biggest iceberg ever seen in the Antarctic was over 335km (208 miles) long and 97km (60 miles) wide.

...and the Antarctic

The continent of Antarctica is a mass of ice resting on a base of solid rock at the **South Pole**. Ninety percent of the world's ice is in Antarctica. This great polar ice sheet is made of snow which has fallen there over thousands of years. This snow covers everything but the sharpest mountain peaks. Even the Ross Sea and the Weddell Sea are covered with ice.

Just as at the North Pole, there is no night or day at the South Pole. Also, every direction from the South Pole leads north.

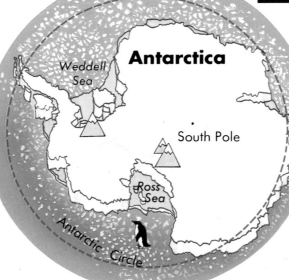

There are more than 50 scientific bases on Antarctica. A **"Sno-cat"** (left) can carry scientists long distances over rough ice and snow. Look for the four caterpillar tracks.

Antarctica was the last continent to be explored. In 1911 **Roald Amundsen** from Norway beat Captain Robert Scott and the British team to the South Pole.